AQA A Level
Physics
Lab Book

Published by Pearson Education Limited, 80 Strand, London, WC2R 0RL.

www.pearsonschoolsandfecolleges.co.uk

Text © Pearson Education Limited 2018
Typeset and illustrated by Tech-Set Ltd Gateshead
Original illustrations © Pearson Education Limited
Cover design by Pete Stratton
Cover photo/illustration © Shutterstock: NaMaKuKi

First published 2018

19 18
10 9 8 7 6 5 4 3 2

British Library Cataloguing in Publication Data
A catalogue record for this book is available from the British Library

ISBN 978 1 292 24530 0

Printed in Italy by LEGO S.p.A

Acknowledgements
The publishers would like to thank John Kavanagh for his contributions to the text.

© Crown Copyright 2016. Public sector information licensed under the Open Government Licence v3.0, *GCE Subject Level Conditions and Requirements for Science (Biology, Chemistry, Physics) and Certificate Requirements, May 2016*

Note from the publisher
Pearson has robust editorial processes, including answer and fact checks, to ensure the accuracy of the content in this publication, and every effort is made to ensure this publication is free of errors. We are, however, only human, and occasionally errors do occur. Pearson is not liable for any misunderstandings that arise as a result of errors in this publication, but it is our priority to ensure that the content is accurate. If you spot an error, please do contact us at resourcescorrections@pearson.com so we can make sure it is corrected.

1 Investigation into the variation of the frequency of stationary waves on a string with length, tension, and mass per unit length of the string

2 Investigation of interference in Young's slit experiment and diffraction by a diffraction grating

3 Determination of g by a free-fall method

4 Determination of the Young modulus by a simple method

5 Determination of resistivity of a wire using a micrometer, ammeter and voltmeter

6 Investigation of the emf and internal resistance of electric cells and batteries by measuring the variation of the terminal pd of the cell with current in it

7 Investigation into simple harmonic motion using a mass–spring system and a simple pendulum

8 Investigation of Boyle's law (constant temperature) and Charles's law (constant pressure) for a gas

9 Investigation of the charge and discharge of capacitors

10 Investigation into how the force on a wire varies with flux density, current and length of wire using a top pan balance

11 Investigation, using a search coil and oscilloscope, of the effect on magnetic flux linkage of varying the angle between a search coil and magnetic field direction

12 Investigation of the inverse-square law for gamma radiation

Practical work can be found at the heart of any science curriculum. It motivates and inspires, links studied theory to real life situations and promotes scientific thinking and understanding. This Lab Book covers practicals from:

- the AQA Physics AS Level course (Practicals 1 to 6)
- the entire AQA Physics A Level course (Practicals 1 to 12).

The experiments and investigations presented fulfil the criteria set out by AQA in the Physics specification. However, it is hoped that students will experience more than the 12 required practical activities prescribed by AQA. This will provide more opportunities to complete CPAC statements and fulfil the various apparatus and techniques criteria.

We have attempted to identify all recognised hazards in the practical activities in this guide. The Lab Book provides suitable warnings about the hazards and suggests appropriate precautions. Teachers and technicians should remember, however, that where there is a hazard, the employer is required to carry out a risk assessment under either the COSHH Regulations or the Management of Health and Safety at Work Regulations. Most education employers have adopted a range of nationally available publications as model (general) risk assessments and, where such published assessments exist for activities, our advice is believed to be compatible with them. We have assumed that practical work is carried out in a properly equipped and maintained laboratory and that any fieldwork takes account of the employer's guidelines. In particular, we have assumed that any mains-operated electrical equipment is properly maintained, that students have been shown how to conduct normal laboratory operations (such as heating or handling heavy objects) safely and that good practice is observed when chemicals or living organisms are handled (see below). We have also assumed that classes are sufficiently small and well-behaved for a teacher to be able to exercise adequate supervision of the students and that rooms are not so crowded that students' activities pose a danger to their neighbours.

CLEAPSS School Science Service are reviewing but not trialling this text. Following receipt of the CLEAPPS review, any guidance on how to make this resource conform to the above policy will be incorporated as the resources are updated.

Important note

Neither Pearson, AQA, the authors nor the series editor take responsibility for the safety of any activity. Before carrying out any practical activity, you are legally required to complete your own risk assessment. In particular, any local rules issued by your employer must be obeyed, regardless of what is recommended in this resource. Where students are required to write their own risk assessments, these must be checked by the teacher and revised, as necessary, to cover any issues the students may have overlooked. The teacher should always have the final control as to how the practical is conducted.

Further sources of information: CLEAPSS www.cleapss.org.uk (includes Secondary Science Laboratory Handbook and Hazcards).

Students have to meet the expectations of the Common Practical Assessment Criteria (CPAC). Students are expected to develop these competencies through the acquisition of technical skills demonstrated in any practical activity undertaken during the course of study. The practical activities will provide opportunities to demonstrate competence in all the skills identified, together with the use of apparatus and practical techniques. Students may work in groups but must be able to demonstrate and record independent evidence of their competency. This must include evidence of independent application of investigative approaches and methods to practical work. Teachers who award a pass to their students need to be confident that the student consistently and routinely exhibits the competencies listed below before completion of the A Level course.

CPAC statements

1 Follows written procedures	a) Correctly follows written instructions to carry out the experimental techniques or procedures.
2 Applies investigative approaches and methods when using instruments and equipment	a) Correctly uses appropriate instrumentation, apparatus and materials (including ICT) to carry out investigative activities, experimental techniques and procedures with minimal assistance or prompting.
	b) Carries out techniques or procedures methodically, in sequence and in combination, identifying practical issues and making adjustments where necessary.
	c) Identifies and controls significant quantitative variables where applicable, and plans approaches to take account of variables that cannot readily be controlled.
	d) Selects appropriate equipment and measurement strategies in order to ensure suitably accurate results.
3 Safely uses a range of practical equipment and materials	a) Identifies hazards and assesses risks associated with those hazards, making safety adjustments as necessary, when carrying out experimental techniques and procedures in the lab or field.
	b) Uses appropriate safety equipment and approaches to minimise risks with minimal prompting.
4 Makes and records observations	a) Makes accurate observations relevant to the experimental or investigative procedure.
	b) Obtains accurate, precise and sufficient data for experimental and investigative procedures and records this methodically using appropriate units and conventions.
5 Researches, references and reports	a) Uses appropriate software and/or tools to process data, carry out research and report findings.
	b) Cites sources of information demonstrating that research has taken place, supporting planning and conclusions.

These practical activities will allow students to develop confidence in the use of apparatus and practical techniques. The table on the following page lists the compulsory elements of the full AQA A Level course. You may wish to tick off each element as you gain confidence.

Apparatus and techniques (AT) statements		1	2	3	4	5	6	7	8	9	10	11	12
AT a	use appropriate analogue apparatus to record a range of measurements (to include length/distance, temperature, pressure, force, angles, volume) and to interpolate between scale markings												
AT b	use appropriate digital instruments, including electrical multimeters, to obtain a range of measurements (to include time, current, voltage, resistance, mass)												
AT c	use methods to increase accuracy of measurements, such as timing over multiple oscillations, or use of fiducial marker, set square or plumb line												
AT d	use stop clock or light gates for timing												
AT e	use calipers and micrometers for small distances, using digital or vernier scales												
AT f	correctly construct circuits from circuit diagrams using dc power supplies, cells, and a range of circuit components, including those where polarity is important												
AT g	design, construct and check circuits using dc power supplies, cells, and a range of circuit components												
AT h	use signal generator and oscilloscope, including volts/division and time-base												
AT i	generate and measure waves, using microphone and loudspeaker, or ripple tank, or vibration transducer, or microwave/radio wave source												
AT j	use laser or light source to investigate characteristics of light, including interference and diffraction												
AT k	use ICT such as computer modelling, or data logger with a variety of sensors to collect data, or use of software to process data												
AT l	use ionising radiation, including detectors												

Source: © Crown Copyright / Department For Education (2015)

Practical 1: Investigation into the variation of the frequency of stationary waves on a string with length, tension, and mass per unit length of the string

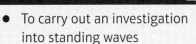

AQA AS and A Level
Physics

AT a, h, i

CPAC links		Evidence	Done
2a	Correctly uses appropriate instrumentation, apparatus and materials (including ICT) to carry out investigative activities, experimental techniques and procedures with minimal assistance or prompting.	Plan and practical procedure	
2b	Carries out techniques or procedures methodically, in sequence and in combination, identifying practical issues and making adjustments where necessary.	Plan and practical procedure	
2c	Identifies and controls significant quantitative variables where applicable, and plans approaches to take account of variables that cannot readily be controlled.	Plan and practical procedure	
2d	Selects appropriate equipment and measurement strategies in order to ensure suitably accurate results.	Plan and practical procedure	
4a	Makes accurate observations relevant to the experimental or investigative procedure.	Practical procedure	
4b	Obtains accurate, precise and sufficient data for experimental and investigative procedures and records this methodically using appropriate units and conventions.	Results and graph	

Objectives

- To carry out an investigation into standing waves
- To develop the skills to carry out further investigations

Equipment

- bench pulley
- slotted masses and hanger
- metre ruler
- 2 m length of rubber 'string'
- vibration generator connected to a signal generator

Safety

- There are no hazards associated with this experiment if rubber is used as the medium. If metal wire is used, safety glasses should be worn.
- Follow the usual electrical precautions for mains-powered apparatus, including a visual inspection of the supply lead.

Procedure

Follow these steps to find the resonant frequency of a rubber 'string'.

1   Attach one end of the string to the vibration generator. Pass the other end of the string over the bench pulley and attach the mass hanger.

2   Add masses until the total mass is 100 g.

3   Turn on the signal generator to set the rubber string oscillating. Move the vibration generator to vary the oscillating length, until resonance is observed.

4   Use a cathode ray oscilloscope (or another suitable method) to obtain an accurate value for the frequency of the signal generator.

In this investigation, you are observing standing waves. These can occur at a variety of resonant frequencies. Investigate the effect on these frequencies of changing different variables – length, tension, and mass per unit length.

Write a detailed plan, outlining which variables you will test and how you will carry out your investigation. Your teacher may need to help you with the details. Record your plan in the space on the following page.

Learning tip

- Length measurements will have a smaller percentage error if you measure as large a length as possible, or as many half-wavelengths as possible.

Practical 1: Investigation into the variation of the frequency of stationary waves on a string with length, tension, and mass per unit length of the string

AQA AS and A Level
Physics

Plan (Use this space to record your plan.)

Practical 1: Investigation into the variation of the frequency of stationary waves on a string with length, tension, and mass per unit length of the string

AQA AS and A Level
Physics

Results (Use this space to record your results.)

Practical 1: Investigation into the variation of the frequency of stationary waves on a string with length, tension, and mass per unit length of the string

AQA AS and A Level
Physics

Analysis of results

1 Draw a graph to show the relationship between one of your variables and the frequency of the stationary wave.

Practical 1: Investigation into the variation of the frequency of stationary waves on a string with length, tension, and mass per unit length of the string

AQA AS and A Level
Physics

Questions

1 Identify the major sources of uncertainty in your work.

....

....

....

....

....

....

....

....

2 Describe any areas of difficulty you encountered while carrying out this investigation and explain how you overcame them.

....

....

....

....

....

....

....

....

....

3 Identify any other safety precautions you might need to take when carrying out this experiment.

....

....

....

....

....

....

AT a, e, j

CPAC links		Evidence	Done
1a	Correctly follows written instructions to carry out the experimental techniques or procedures.	Practical procedure	
2a	Correctly uses appropriate instrumentation, apparatus and materials (including ICT) to carry out investigative activities, experimental techniques and procedures with minimal assistance or prompting.	Practical procedure	
4a	Makes accurate observations relevant to the experimental or investigative procedure.	Results	

Objective

To determine the wavelength of laser light using Young's fringes

Equipment

- laser
- slide with double slit 'rulings'
- white screen
- paper
- mounting material
- metre ruler
- optional: vernier microscope

Safety ⚠️

- Lasers should be Class 2 and have a maximum output of 1 mW. They present little risk in the laboratory, provided sensible precautions are taken to reduce the risk of accidentally shining the light into eyes.
- CLEAPSS *Laboratory Handbook* section 12.12 and publication PS52 are helpful.
- Follow the usual electrical precautions for mains-powered apparatus, including a visual inspection of the supply lead.

Part A: Young's 'double slit' interference experiment

Procedure

1 Set up a laser and double slit slide, as shown in Figure A. You can shine the light onto a wall rather than a screen, but the surface must be matt to prevent too much of the beam being reflected in one direction. The distance, D, between the double slit slide and the screen should be approximately 1 metre.

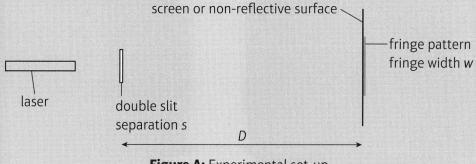

Figure A: Experimental set-up

2 Move the laser so that the light shines through the double slit slide. An interference pattern should be visible on the screen.

3 Measure the fringe spacing, w, over a large number of visible fringes. (Measure across several fringes and divide this measurement by the number of fringes.) The best way to do this is to attach a sheet of paper to the screen (or wall), mark fringes on it, then remove the paper and measure over a large number of fringes.

4 Measure the distance, D.

5 Repeat steps 1 to 4, varying the distance D.

6 Make a note of the slit separation, s. This may be printed on the slide; if not, use a travelling or vernier microscope to measure this distance.

Results (Use this space to record all of your results.)

Analysis of results

1 Draw a graph of *w* against *D*. This should produce a straight line with the gradient $= \frac{\lambda}{s}$.

2 Use the gradient of your graph to determine the wavelength of the laser light.

Part B: Diffraction grating

Procedure

1 Place the laser approximately 4 m away from a large wall and place the diffraction grating in front of the laser. The laser beam should pass through the grating at normal incidence and meet the wall perpendicularly.

2 Measure the distance, D, between the grating and the wall.

3 Turn on the laser and identify the zero-order maximum (straight through the grating).

4 Measure the distance x from the zero-order maximum to the first-order maxima (the closest maxima either side of the zero-order maximum). Calculate the mean of these two values. This is the maximum produced according to $n = 1$ using the equation $n\lambda = d\sin\theta$. (Remember, d is the distance between slits in the diffraction grating.)

5 Then measure the distance x for increasing orders.

6 Use your values of x and D to determine θ using $\tan\theta = \dfrac{x}{D}$ for each maximum.

Learning tip

- Ensure that the laser hits the wall at a right angle.

Results (Use this space to record your results.)

Analysis of results (Use your results to determine a mean value for the wavelength of the laser light. Compare your calculated value with the accepted wavelength for a standard school red laser, 635 nm. You could also estimate the uncertainty in your value.)

Questions

1   Explain why a metre ruler with a precision of 1 mm is suitable for measuring the distances in this experiment.

....

....

....

....

2   Describe the diffraction pattern that would be produced if a narrow bright white light source was used instead of the laser.

....

....

....

....

3   Explain how the interference would be different if a green laser was used instead of a red laser.

....

....

....

4   In Part B, you estimated the uncertainty in your value for the wavelength of the laser light. What could you have done in the experiment to reduce this uncertainty?

....

....

....

AT	a, c, d

CPAC links		Evidence	Done
2a	Correctly uses appropriate instrumentation, apparatus and materials (including ICT) to carry out investigative activities, experimental techniques and procedures with minimal assistance or prompting.	Practical procedure	
2b	Carries out techniques or procedures methodically, in sequence and in combination, identifying practical issues and making adjustments where necessary.	Practical procedure	
2d	Selects appropriate equipment and measurement strategies in order to ensure suitably accurate results.	Results	
4b	Obtains accurate, precise and sufficient data for experimental and investigative procedures and records this methodically using appropriate units and conventions.	Graphs	

Objectives

To measure the acceleration due to gravity *g* of an object falling freely and to consider the following alternative methods:
- object falling through a trap door
- object falling through a light gate

Equipment

- metre ruler or tape measure with millimetre resolution
- iron sphere
- electronic timer
- electromagnet to retain iron sphere
- two light gates (optional)
- clamp and stand
- low voltage power supply
- trap door switch

Safety

- Ensure security of any apparatus that might topple over. A G-clamp can assist here.
- Be aware of falling objects.
- Turn off the electromagnet when it is not in use, as it will get hot.

It is difficult to produce a free-falling object in a laboratory, because the object will experience air resistance as it falls. For an object to be truly free-falling, there must be no other forces acting on it.

However, if the object is made of a suitably dense substance, and its speed is not disproportionate, it can be considered to be falling freely. This means you can use the appropriate SUVAT equation to calculate *g*.

Procedure

1 Set up your equipment as shown in Figure A. (If you have access to light gates, your teacher may direct you to an alternative method.)

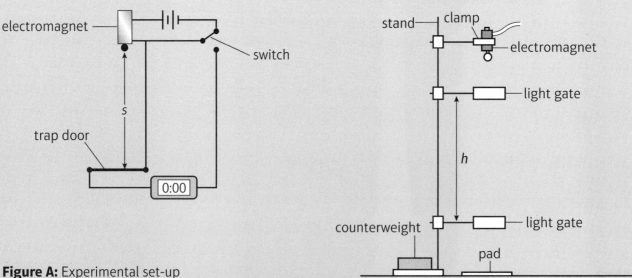

Figure A: Experimental set-up

2 Drop the object from rest and record the time taken, *t*, for the sphere to fall to the trap door switch.

3 Repeat step 2 twice more and calculate the mean value of *t*.

4 Measure and record the height, *h*, fallen by the object.

5 Vary the height and repeat steps **2–4**. Take readings at a minimum of six different heights.

6 For each height, calculate the range in your readings for *t*. Divide this value by 2 to find the uncertainty in *t*, then calculate the percentage uncertainty in *t*.

Method alteration (If you make any alterations to the method, make a note of these changes in this space.)

Results (Record your results in the space below.)

Graph

The SUVAT equation $s = ut + \frac{1}{2}at^2$, where $u = 0$, $a = g$ and $s = h$, produces $h = \frac{1}{2}gt^2$.

This can be rearranged to $t^2 = \frac{2h}{g}$. Comparison with $y = mx + c$ shows that a graph of t^2 against h should be a straight line passing through the origin, with gradient $\frac{2}{g}$.

Plot a graph of t^2 against h on the following page. Alternatively, you may use a computer to produce your graph. If you do this, print out your graph and attach it on the following page.

Analysis of results (Use the gradient of your graph to determine a value for *g*.)

Graph (Plot a graph of t^2 against h here.)

Questions

1 State an advantage of using light gates in this experiment.

....

....

2 State the effect of air resistance on your value for g.

....

....

3 Explain why the graph of t^2 against h should be a straight line.

....

....

....

4 What other safety precaution should be taken in this experiment?

....

....

....

5 Estimate the uncertainty in your value for g. What is the most likely cause of this uncertainty?

....

....

....

....

6 When plotting your graph, the line of best fit should pass through the origin.

    a If the line intercepts the y-axis with a slight positive value, what could this mean?

....

....

....

....

    b Why should you not force the line of best fit through the origin?

....

....

....

AT **a, e**

CPAC links		Evidence	Done
1a	Correctly follows written instructions to carry out the experimental techniques or procedures.	Practical observation	
2a	Correctly uses appropriate instrumentation, apparatus and materials (including ICT) to carry out investigative activities, experimental techniques and procedures with minimal assistance or prompting.	Practical observation	
2b	Carries out techniques or procedures methodically, in sequence and in combination, identifying practical issues and making adjustments where necessary.	Method followed	
4b	Obtains accurate, precise and sufficient data for experimental and investigative procedures and records this methodically using appropriate units and conventions.	Results and graph	
5a	Uses appropriate software and/or tools to process data, carry out research and report findings.	Results, graph and conclusions	
5b	Cites sources of information demonstrating that research has taken place, supporting planning and conclusions.	Relevant references	

Research

There are two methods that can be used to determine the Young modulus of a wire: one suspends the test wire from the ceiling, while the other requires the test wire to be stretched horizontally.

Write a method for each procedure, including diagrams to show how the apparatus is used in each case. Your teacher will confirm which method you should use in your investigation.

Objective

To determine the Young modulus of a material by a simple method

Equipment

- 32 swg steel wire
- 28 swg copper wire
- 32 swg copper wire
- scale and vernier arrangement with integral clamps for the wires
- scale and marker
- micrometer screw gauge
- metre ruler
- masses and mass holders
- safety goggles
- two wooden blocks and clamp
- bench pulley
- 90° set square

Safety

- Wear safety goggles.
- Place a tray of sand or newspapers below weights.
- Do not stand close to where the weights can drop.

Results (Record your results in a suitable table in the space below.)

Graph (Plot a graph of mean extension against load.)

Analysis of results

1   Use the gradient of your graph to calculate the Young modulus for the wire you tested.

Learning tip

Uncertainty is the range over which the true value can be expected to lie, with a given level of confidence or probability. Uncertainty gives an indication of the accuracy of a value.

2   Estimate the uncertainty in your value for the Young modulus.

Questions

1   Explain whether it is appropriate to state your value for the Young modulus of your wire to two significant figures.

....

....

....

....

....

2   Why should you wear safety goggles throughout the practical?

....

....

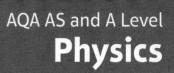

3 If you carried out the vertical method, you would have suspended two wires from the ceiling.

   a What is the second wire?

....

....

   b Explain the purpose of the second wire.

....

....

....

....

4 Why do you need to ensure the testing wire is free from kinks?

....

....

5 What step in your method ensures that the limit of proportionality is not exceeded?

....

....

....

....

....

6 Why should the test wire be as long and thin as possible?

....

....

....

7 How did you calculate the cross-sectional area of the wire you tested?

....

....

....

8 Why is the vertical experiment more suitable for testing steel than the horizontal method?

....

....

....

Practical 5: Determination of resistivity of a wire using a micrometer, ammeter and voltmeter

AT b, e, f

CPAC links		Evidence	Done
1a	Correctly follows written instructions to carry out the experimental techniques or procedures.	Practical observation	
2a	Correctly uses appropriate instrumentation, apparatus and materials (including ICT) to carry out investigative activities, experimental techniques and procedures with minimal assistance or prompting.	Practical observation	
2b	Carries out techniques or procedures methodically, in sequence and in combination, identifying practical issues and making adjustments where necessary.	Method followed	
4b	Obtains accurate, precise and sufficient data for experimental and investigative procedures and records this methodically using appropriate units and conventions.	Results and graph	
5a	Uses appropriate software and/or tools to process data, carry out research and report findings.	Results, graph and conclusions	
5b	Cites sources of information demonstrating that research has taken place, supporting planning and conclusions.	Relevant references	

Objectives

- To determine the resistivity of a wire using $\rho = A \times \frac{R}{l}$
- To develop the skills to carry out further investigations

Equipment

- ammeter
- voltmeter
- power pack (low voltage variable dc)
- 22 swg constantan wire
- crocodile clips
- connecting leads
- metre ruler
- micrometer

Safety

With a high current, the wire can get hot. Do not touch the wire while the power is switched on, and switch off the power if you smell burning.

Procedure

1 Use a micrometer to measure the diameter of the constantan wire. Take measurements in at least three places and in different directions to work out the mean diameter, *d*. Convert this value to metres.

2 Set up your equipment as shown in Figure A.

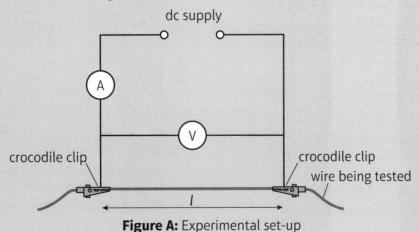

Figure A: Experimental set-up

3 Tape the wire to the metre ruler and attach one crocodile clip at 0.

4 Touch the other crocodile clip to the wire at 0.1 m. Measure the current, *I*, with the voltage, *V*, at 0.5 V. Remove the second crocodile clip as soon as you have measured the current: the short length of wire will get very hot. Switch off the circuit between readings.

5 Measure the current and voltage several times for this length of wire, then use your values of *I* and *V* to calculate the mean resistance, *R*, for this length of wire.

6 Repeat steps **4–5**, placing the second crocodile clip at 0.1 m intervals up to 0.8 m. You will need to alter the voltage to try to keep the current around 0.5 A.

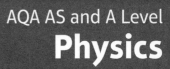
Cross-sectional area of wire (Use the diameter of the wire (measured in Step 1) to calculate the cross-sectional area, A, using the formula $A = \frac{\pi d^2}{4}$.)

Results (Use this space to record your results.)

Analysis of results

1 Plot a graph of mean resistance (R) against length of wire (l).

2 Find the gradient of your graph, $\frac{\rho}{A}$. Use this value, and your calculated value of A, to calculate the resistivity (ρ) of the tested wire.

3 Determine the uncertainty in your values for the gradient and A. Hence, calculate the uncertainty in your value for the resistivity. Remember, you will have to use percentage uncertainties when combining them.

4 Find values of ρ from two different sources and cite these sources in an appropriate format; one should be online and one from elsewhere. With reference to the uncertainties you calculated, comment on your value for ρ.

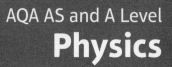

Questions

1 What is the unit of resistivity?

....

2 Why is it good practice to measure the diameter of the wire in several places and in different directions?

....

....

....

....

3 Identify the sources of uncertainty in this experiment. Consider the accuracy (percentage difference) of your result and comment on the effect the uncertainties might have had.

....

....

....

....

....

....

....

....

....

....

....

4 Explain why the current through the wire should be small.

....

....

....

....

5 If the wire being tested becomes warm (i.e. at very short lengths) this could alter the resistivity of the wire. What can be done to overcome this problem?

....

....

....

....

Practical 6: Investigation of the emf and internal resistance of electric cells and batteries by measuring the variation of the terminal pd of the cell with current in it

AQA AS and A Level
Physics

AT | b, f

CPAC links		Evidence	Done
2a	Correctly uses appropriate instrumentation, apparatus and materials (including ICT) to carry out investigative activities, experimental techniques and procedures with minimal assistance or prompting.	Practical procedure	
2b	Carries out techniques or procedures methodically, in sequence and in combination, identifying practical issues and making adjustments where necessary.	Practical procedure	
2d	Selects appropriate equipment and measurement strategies in order to ensure suitably accurate results.	Diagram	
3a	Identifies hazards and assesses risks associated with those hazards, making safety adjustments as necessary, when carrying out experimental techniques and procedures in the lab or field.	Practical procedure	
4b	Obtains accurate, precise and sufficient data for experimental and investigative procedures and records this methodically using appropriate units and conventions.	Graph	

Objective

To make measurements using an electrical circuit

Equipment

- voltmeter on 2 V range
- ammeter on 200 mA range
- connecting leads
- electrical cell such as a 1.5 V cell (avoid using brand new or very old cells)
- variable resistor

Safety

- Do NOT use rechargeable batteries, due to the risk of short circuit. See CLEAPSS guidance leaflet GL225 for advice on using batteries in general practical circuit work.
- Follow normal laboratory safety procedures.

Procedure

1 Set up the circuit shown in Figure A.

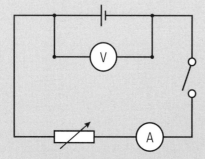

Figure A: Circuit diagram

2 With the switch open, take a reading for the potential difference, V, on the voltmeter.

3 Close the switch to take subsequent readings of potential difference and current, I – but only close the switch when taking readings. Do not leave the circuit on when not recording values.

4 Alter the variable resistor and record the current and potential difference. Take a minimum of six readings, at different values of resistance.

Learning tip

- It is not usually necessary to repeat readings from an electrical circuit like this. There is very little random error and very little judgement is required when taking readings. For this reason, you should take more than the usual six readings if possible, so you have more points on your graph. This will make it easier to recognise any anomalies.

Practical 6: Investigation of the emf and internal resistance of electric cells and batteries by measuring the variation of the terminal pd of the cell with current in it

AQA AS and A Level
Physics

Results (Use this space to record your results.)

Analysis of results

The mathematical model for this circuit is $\varepsilon = I(R + r)$. We know that $V = IR$ so this produces $\varepsilon = V + Ir$. On the following page, plot a graph of V against I. This should give a straight line with gradient $-r$. Find the gradient and use this value to determine ε.

Practical 6: Investigation of the emf and internal resistance of electric cells and batteries by measuring the variation of the terminal pd of the cell with current in it

AQA AS and A Level
Physics

Graph (Plot a graph of *V* against *I*.)

Practical 6: Investigation of the emf and internal resistance of electric cells and batteries by measuring the variation of the terminal pd of the cell with current in it

AQA AS and A Level
Physics

Questions

1   The *y*-axis intercept of your graph will be very close to the true value for the emf of the cell. Account for any difference.

....

....

....

....

2   What is internal resistance? How does it occur?

....

....

....

....

....

....

3   What is the difference between emf and terminal pd?

....

....

....

....

....

....

....

4   What is meant by 'lost volts'?

....

....

....

5   What would you see in the results if there was no internal resistance?

....

....

....

....

AT **a, b, c**

CPAC links		Evidence	Done
1a	Correctly follows written instructions to carry out the experimental techniques or procedures.	Practical procedure	
2b	Carries out techniques or procedures methodically, in sequence and in combination, identifying practical issues and making adjustments where necessary.	Practical procedure	
2d	Selects appropriate equipment and measurement strategies in order to ensure suitably accurate results.	Practical procedure	
4b	Obtains accurate, precise and sufficient data for experimental and investigative procedures and records this methodically using appropriate units and conventions.	Results table	
5a	Uses appropriate software and/or tools to process data, carry out research and report findings.	Spreadsheet and graph	

Objective

To investigate the factors affecting the time period of a simple pendulum

Equipment

- three pendulum bobs of different mass
- long string
- metre ruler
- retort stand with clamp and boss
- two small wooden blocks
- stop clock
- optical pins or similar
- adhesive putty

Safety

- If you have been provided with optical pins, take care with the points.
- It is recommended to use a G-clamp to secure the retort stand and prevent it from tipping over.

Part A: Simple pendulum

Procedure

1. Set up the apparatus as shown in Figure A. It is difficult to see from the diagram, but the pendulum bob string should be clamped between two small wooden blocks. The fiducial marker could also be a piece of card with a line drawn on it, attached to the stand behind the pendulum.

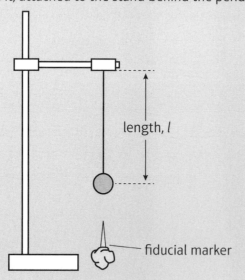

length, *l*

fiducial marker

Figure A: Experimental set-up

2. Measure the pendulum length, *l*, from the top of the bob to the point where it is attached to the clamp. Then measure the radius of the bob and add this value to your first measurement to give the correct value of *l*.

3. Place the fiducial marker directly under the bob. This will mark the centre of each oscillation as the pendulum oscillates.

4. Prepare a suitable results table in the space on the following page.

5 Set the length of the string to 0.2 m and time ten complete oscillations, using the fiducial marker as a guide. Start the timer as the bob passes the marker, count ten complete cycles, then stop the timer as the bob passes the marker at the end of the tenth oscillation. Keep the angle of swing small (under 10°).

6 Record the time for ten oscillations, then find the average time for one oscillation and record this as the time period, T.

7 Repeat steps 5 and 6, extending the string in steps of 0.2 m, up to 1.0 m.

8 Repeat steps 5 to 7 using two other pendulum bobs of different mass.

Learning tip

● When timing the oscillations, let the first one or two go before starting to time. This avoids the issue of trying to release the bob and start the stop clock at the same time.

Results (Use this space to record your results.)

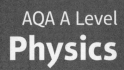
Analysis of results

1 For each pendulum, plot a graph with T^2 on the y-axis and length l on the x-axis. To complete CPAC 5a, you should use a spreadsheet package to produce your graphs. If you do this, print out your graphs and attach them here.

2 Theory suggests that the time period for a simple pendulum is independent of the mass of the bob, but dependent on the length: $T = 2\pi\sqrt{\dfrac{l}{g}}$. If this theory is correct, each set of results should produce a straight line graph with gradient $\dfrac{4\pi^2}{g}$. Use your graphs to determine a value for the acceleration due to gravity, g, using the equation $g = \dfrac{4\pi^2}{\text{gradient}}$.

3 Calculate the percentage uncertainty in your value for g.

Questions

1 Why should you keep the angle of swing small?

....

....

2 What is the velocity of the pendulum at its end points?

....

....

3 When is the velocity of the pendulum at its maximum?

....

....

4 At what point does the pendulum have maximum potential energy?

....

....

5 At what point does the pendulum have maximum kinetic energy?

....

....

6 Galileo Galilei was the first person to study the properties of pendulums in 1602. Conduct some research and summarise what he found out. Cite your sources using an appropriate format.

....

....

....

....

....

....

....

....

....

....

....

CPAC links		Evidence	Done
1a	Correctly follows written instructions to carry out the experimental techniques or procedures.	Practical procedure	
2b	Carries out techniques or procedures methodically, in sequence and in combination, identifying practical issues and making adjustments where necessary.	Practical procedure	
4b	Obtains accurate, precise and sufficient data for experimental and investigative procedures and records this methodically using appropriate units and conventions.	Results table	

Part B: Mass–spring system

Procedure

1 Set up the apparatus as shown in the diagram. The fiducial marker should be level with the bottom of the mass. This will become the centre of the oscillations.

2 Prepare a suitable results table in the space provided.

3 Hang a mass of 0.1 kg from the spring. Create a small displacement and time ten oscillations.

4 Calculate the time for one oscillation and record this as *T*.

5 Repeat steps **3** and **4** with 0.2 kg, 0.3 kg, 0.4 kg and 0.5 kg masses.

Results (Use this space to record your results.)

Objective

To investigate the time period of a mass–spring system

Equipment

- retort stand, boss and clamp
- helical spring
- selection of masses
- stop clock

Safety ⚠

As this is a mass–spring system, use a G-clamp to prevent the retort stand tipping over.

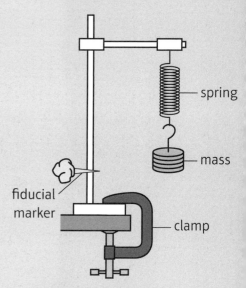

Figure A: Experimental set-up

Learning tips

- When you displace the mass on the spring, try to limit the displacement and avoid setting the spring swinging from side to side.
- Do not extend the spring beyond its elastic limit.

Analysis of results

1 Plot a graph with mass, *m*, on the *x*-axis and T^2 on the *y*-axis. This should produce a straight line.

2   The equation for the time period of a mass-spring system is $T = 2\pi\sqrt{\frac{m}{k}}$, where k is the spring constant or stiffness of the spring.

This can be rearranged to $T^2 = \frac{4\pi^2 m}{k}$. Find the gradient of the graph and use this to determine k.

Questions

1   Why is it better to draw a graph of m against T^2 rather than m against T?

....

....

....

....

2   What other safety precautions would you need to take in this experiment?

....

....

3   Why is it better to time ten oscillations when finding the time period?

....

....

4   The term 'equilibrium point' can be used to describe the point at which you place the fiducial mark. What does this mean and why place the fiducial mark here?

....

....

....

....

....

....

AT a, e, k

CPAC links		Evidence	Done
1a	Correctly follows written instructions to carry out the experimental techniques or procedures.	Practical procedure	
2a	Correctly uses appropriate instrumentation, apparatus and materials (including ICT) to carry out investigative activities, experimental techniques and procedures with minimal assistance or prompting.	Practical procedure	
4b	Obtains accurate, precise and sufficient data for experimental and investigative procedures and records this methodically using appropriate units and conventions.	Measurements and results table	

Objective °

To explore the relationship between pressure, volume and temperature for gases (Boyle's law)

Equipment
- Boyle's law apparatus
- pump

Safety ⚠

The sealed tube used in this practical should be protected within a Perspex® tube. Check with your teacher if in doubt.

Part A: Boyle's law

Procedure

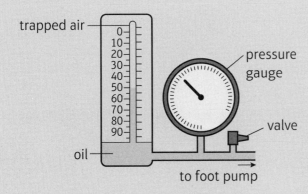

Figure A: Apparatus used to demonstrate the relationship between pressure and volume

1. Using the apparatus provided, take a reading for the pressure on the gauge and a reading for the volume of air in the tube. Record your results in a suitable table in the space provided on p.46.

2. Connect the pump to the apparatus.

3. Use the pump to increase the pressure by approximately 10 kPa, then take the new pressure and volume readings.

4. Repeat step **3** until you have at least five more sets of readings. Pause between readings to let the gas cool down.

5. Reduce the pressure again, in steps of approximately 10 kPa. Take another set of readings as you reduce the pressure.

Results (Use this space to record your results.)

Graph (Plot a graph with pressure, *p*, on the *x*-axis and *1/V* on the *y*-axis.)

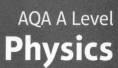
Questions

1 What other safety precautions do you need to take in this experiment?

....

....

2 Name the variables in this experiment:

   a independent ....

   b dependent ....

   c control ....

3 What would be the effect of an increase in temperature, *T*, on:

   a the volume at constant pressure

....

....

   b the pressure at constant volume?

....

....

4 Which conditions are required to ensure the experiment is testing Boyle's law?

....

....

....

....

....

....

....

....

5 Does your graph confirm Boyle's law?

....

....

....

....

CPAC links		Evidence	Done
1a	Correctly follows written instructions to carry out the experimental techniques or procedures.	Practical procedure	
2b	Carries out techniques or procedures methodically, in sequence and in combination, identifying practical issues and making adjustments where necessary.	Practical procedure and answers to questions	
2c	Identifies and controls significant quantitative variables where applicable, and plans approaches to take account of variables that cannot readily be controlled.	Practical procedure and answers to questions	
3b	Uses appropriate safety equipment and approaches to minimise risks with minimal prompting.	Practical procedure	
4b	Obtains accurate, precise and sufficient data for experimental and investigative procedures and records this methodically using appropriate units and conventions.	Measurements and results table	

Objective

To estimate absolute zero

Equipment

- beaker
- kettle
- 30 cm ruler
- capillary tube with plug of acid or mercury
- thermometer
- clamp

Safety

- Take care with the heated water, especially as the beaker will have tall objects in it.
- The capillary tube contains concentrated sulfuric acid or mercury (see CLEAPSS Hazcard HC062). This, plus the very hot water, means eye protection should be worn. CLEAPSS Guide R231 provides further guidance.
- Always follow your teacher's instructions carefully.

Part B: Charles's law

Procedure

1 Set up the apparatus as shown in Figure A. Remember that the capillary tube contains a drop of concentrated sulfuric acid or mercury and must be handled with care. The capillary tube can be secured to the ruler using rubber bands.

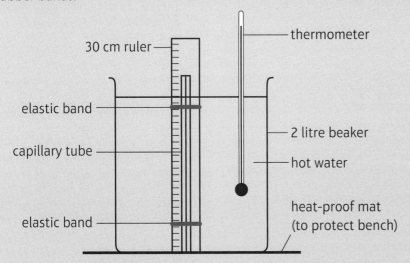

Figure A: Apparatus to test Charles's law

2 Measure and record the height of the column of air, h. This is measured from the bottom of the capillary tube to the drop of acid.

3 Use a kettle to boil water, then allow the water to cool slightly to prevent the ruler from warping. Add the hot water to the beaker.

4 Stir the water with the thermometer and record both h and θ as the temperature decreases. Try to take measurements roughly every 5 °C, until there is a constant temperature.

Results (Use this space to record your results.)

Analysis of results

1 On the following page, plot a graph with θ on the x-axis and h on the y-axis.

2 Find the gradient of your graph, m.

3 Use your graph to estimate a value for absolute zero.

....

4 Work out the percentage difference between your answer to question 3 and the accepted value for absolute zero.

Graph (Plot a graph with θ on the *x*-axis and *h* on the *y*-axis. You will need to ensure the *x*-axis values range from −300 °C to +100 °C. Extrapolate the line until it crosses the *x*-axis and record this temperature, $\theta = 0$ K.)

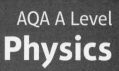

Questions

1 What could you do to obtain readings below room temperature?

....

....

2 The plug of sulfuric acid traps the air below it, and also keeps the air dry. Why is this important?

....

....

3 The experiment assumes that the pressure of the air trapped in the capillary tube remains constant during the experiment. Why is this a valid assumption?

....

....

....

....

....

....

....

....

4 What happens when a real gas cools?

....

5 What is meant by absolute zero?

....

....

6 Calculate the difference between your value for absolute zero and the accepted value.

....

....

....

....

7 Suggest some reasons for the difference between the two values.

....

....

....

....

AT	a, b, d, f, g, k

CPAC links		Evidence	Done
1a	Correctly follows written instructions to carry out the experimental techniques or procedures.	Practical procedure	
3a	Identifies hazards and assesses risks associated with those hazards, making safety adjustments as necessary, when carrying out experimental techniques and procedures in the lab or field.	Practical procedure	
4b	Obtains accurate, precise and sufficient data for experimental and investigative procedures and records this methodically using appropriate units and conventions.	Graph	

Part A: Discharging

Procedure

1   Set up your circuit as shown in Figure A.

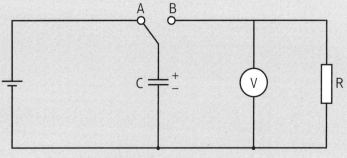

Figure A: Circuit set-up

2   To charge the capacitor, set the two-pole switch to position A. The charging current is usually at a safe value, because it is limited by the internal resistance of the battery. However, the capacitor will charge up almost instantly.

3   Move the switch to position B to discharge the capacitor, C, through the resistor, R. Use this procedure to check that all components are working as expected.

4   Charge up the capacitor. Then move the switch to position B and, at the same time, start the stop clock. Record the voltage reading at time zero ($t = 0$). Then take further readings at 5 second intervals as the capacitor discharges.

5   Repeat step **4** with different resistors. Your teacher may also ask you to repeat this step with different capacitors.

Objectives

- To discharge a capacitor through a resistor
- To charge a capacitor through a resistor

Equipment

- voltmeter
- ammeter
- capacitors (suitable values: $4700\,\mu F$, $2200\,\mu F$, $1000\,\mu F$)
- resistors
- battery (1.5 V or half the voltage rating of the capacitor)
- SPDT switch
- connecting leads
- stop clock

Safety

- Do not exceed the voltage rating of the capacitor. Voltage must be less than 40 V DC.
- Take care to avoid any short circuits.
- Make sure electrolytic capacitors are connected the correct way around.

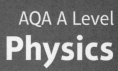

Results (Use this space to record your results.)

Analysis of results

1 Plot a graph of V (pd across the capacitor) against t. This should produce an exponential decay curve, as given by the equation $V = V_0 e^{-\frac{t}{RC}}$.

2 Plot a graph of ln V against t. This should produce a straight line graph with gradient $-\frac{1}{RC}$.

3 Find the gradient of your graph and use this to determine C.

Part B: Charging

Procedure

1   Set up your circuit as shown in Figure B. The voltmeter should read zero with the capacitor uncharged.

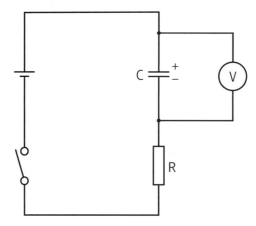

Figure B: Circuit set-up

2   To charge the capacitor, close the switch. Record the voltage at 5 second intervals as the capacitor charges.

3   Repeat step **2** using different resistors and capacitors.

Results (Use this space to record your results.)

Graph (Plot a graph of pd across the capacitor against time.)

59

Questions

1 In the equation $V = V_0 e^{-\frac{t}{RC}}$, what is RC?

....

....

....

....

....

2 The values printed on resistors and capacitors are known as 'nominal values'. What does this mean?

....

....

....

....

....

3 Both of the graphs produced in Part A allow you to calculate C. Why does the second graph (ln V against t) produce a more accurate value?

....

....

....

....

....

....

4 You could have used a computer with a voltage sensor connected to a data logger to take readings. What would be the advantages of this method, compared with the method you used?

....

....

....

....

....

....

....

Practical 10: Investigation into how the force on a wire varies with flux density, current and length of wire using a top pan balance

AQA A Level
Physics

AT a, b, c

CPAC links		Evidence	Done
1a	Correctly follows written instructions to carry out the experimental techniques or procedures.	Practical procedure	
3a	Identifies hazards and assesses risks associated with those hazards, making safety adjustments as necessary, when carrying out experimental techniques and procedures in the lab or field.	Practical procedure	
4b	Obtains accurate, precise and sufficient data for experimental and investigative procedures and records this methodically using appropriate units and conventions.	Graph	

Objective

To investigate the relationship between force, magnetic flux density, current and length

Equipment

- power supply (low voltage dc)
- ammeter
- thick copper wire
- clamp stands
- crocodile clips
- connecting leads
- four magnadur magnets with a metal cradle
- electronic top pan balance
- 30 cm ruler

Safety ⚠

- Take care, as the equipment may become warm.
- Turn off the circuit between readings.

Procedure

1 Set up your equipment as shown in Figure A. Your teacher may have prepared a set-up for you to look at, to make it easier to assemble the various parts correctly.

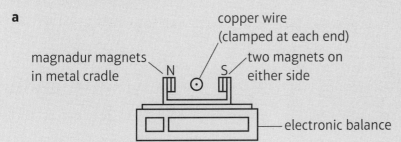

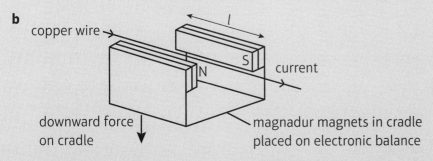

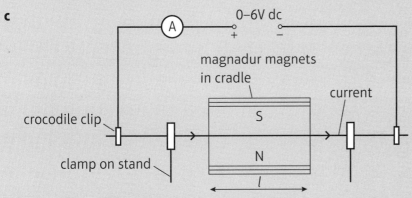

Figure A: (a) End view, (b) side view and (c) top view

2 With no current flowing in the circuit, zero the balance.

3 Increase the voltage on the power supply to obtain a current, I, of 6.0 A (as read from the ammeter). This should be treated as a maximum.

Practical 10: Investigation into how the force on a wire varies with flux density, current and length of wire using a top pan balance

AQA A Level
Physics

4 Record the value on the balance, *m,* in grams.

5 Repeat steps **3** and **4** to obtain values for *I* at 1 A intervals from 5.0 A to 1.0 A.

6 Repeat the whole experiment. Use your second set of results to calculate a mean value of *m* for each value of *I*.

Results (Use the space below to record your results.)

Practical 10: Investigation into how the force on a wire varies with flux density, current and length of wire using a top pan balance

AQA A Level
Physics

Analysis of results

1 Plot a graph of *m* against current, *I*. Draw a line of best fit through the points. This line should pass through the origin.

2 Find the gradient of the line of best fit.

Practical 10: Investigation into how the force on a wire varies with flux density, current and length of wire using a top pan balance

AQA A Level
Physics
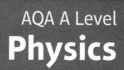

The force F (N) acting on a wire of length L (m), with a current I (A) passing through it, in a magnetic field with flux density B (T) at an angle θ to the field is given by: $F = BIL \sin \theta$.

The force on the wire will have its maximum value when the wire is perpendicular to the field lines. At this point, $\theta = 90°$, so and the force on the wire, $F = BIL$.

We also know that $F = mg$ (mass × acceleration due to gravity). We can link these equations to produce:

$$BIL = mg$$

In this investigation, m has been recorded in grams. However, g is 9.81 Nkg^{-1}, so mg must be divided by 1000:

$$BIL = \frac{mg}{1000}$$

This can be rearranged to:

$$B = \frac{mg}{I \times L \times 1000}$$

To find L, we must measure the length of the magnadur magnets in metres.

The gradient of the graph gives $\frac{m}{I}$. Therefore, the value for gradient can be substituted into the equation to produce a new equation:

$$B = \frac{\text{gradient} \times g}{L \times 1000}$$

3 Find a value for B.

4 The value obtained for B is typically around 5×10^{-2} Tesla. How does your value compare to this?

....

....

....

....

....

....

....

Practical 10: Investigation into how the force on a wire varies with flux density, current and length of wire using a top pan balance

AQA A Level
Physics
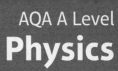

Questions

1   Discuss the issues with this experiment which might have led you to calculate an inaccurate value of *B*.

....

....

....

....

....

....

....

....

....

....

....

....

2   Why must the wire be perpendicular to the field lines?

....

....

....

....

3   Define magnetic flux density.

....

....

....

....

....

....

4   Why should the balance be zeroed when there is no current passing through the wire?

....

....

....

Practical 11: Investigation, using a search coil and oscilloscope, of the effect on magnetic flux linkage of varying the angle between a search coil and magnetic field direction

AQA A Level
Physics

AT a, h

CPAC links		Evidence	Done
1a	Correctly follows written instructions to carry out the experimental techniques or procedures.	Practical procedure	
3a	Identifies hazards and assesses risks associated with those hazards, making safety adjustments as necessary, when carrying out experimental techniques and procedures in the lab or field.	Practical procedure	
4b	Obtains accurate, precise and sufficient data for experimental and investigative procedures and records this methodically using appropriate units and conventions.	Graph	

Objective

To investigate the relationship between magnetic flux linkage and angle

Equipment

- oscilloscope
- power supply (low voltage ac)
- large circular coil and stand
- connecting leads
- protractor
- search coil and stand

Safety

- Take care, as the equipment may become warm.
- Turn off the circuit between readings.

Flux linkage can be calculated using the equation:

$$BAN \cos \theta = \text{flux linkage}$$

where N is the number of turns in a coil of area A with its axis at an angle θ to a magnetic field of strength B.

In the set-up shown in Figure A, the search coil is clamped so that the plane of the coil is parallel to the plane of the large circular coil, and perpendicular to the field lines produced by the circular coil. This will produce the maximum induced emf in the search coil and the maximum flux linkage with $\cos \theta = 1$.

Procedure

1. Set up your equipment as shown in Figure A. Your teacher may have prepared a set-up for you to look at, to make it easier to assemble the various parts correctly.

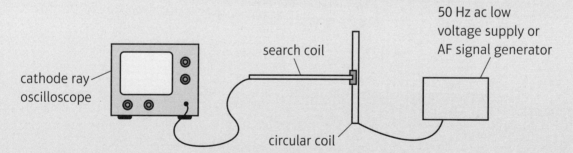
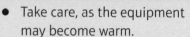

Figure A: Experimental set-up

2. Switch off the time base on the oscilloscope so that the induced emf is displayed as a vertical line. Measure the length of this line.

3. Divide this length by two to calculate the amplitude of the induced emf. (Refer to the y-gain setting on the oscilloscope.)

4. Alter the angle of the search coil (the angle between the plane of the circular coil and the plane of the search coil). Record the angle of the search coil and the peak value of the induced emf.

5. Repeat step 4 for at least ten different angles. If you have time, try to take measurements every 20°.

Learning tip

- You could clamp a large protractor behind the search coil support rod to help you measure the angle of the search coil.

Practical 11: Investigation, using a search coil and oscilloscope, of the effect on magnetic flux linkage of varying the angle between a search coil and magnetic field direction

AQA A Level
Physics

Results (Use the space below to record your results in a suitable format.)

Analysis of results

1   In the space on the following page, plot a graph showing how the flux linkage (on the y-axis) varies with the angle of the coil (on the x-axis).

2   Calculate the maximum value of the peak flux linkage.

Practical 11: Investigation, using a search coil and oscilloscope, of the effect on magnetic flux linkage of varying the angle between a search coil and magnetic field direction

AQA A Level
Physics

Graph (Plot a graph showing flux linkage (on the *y*-axis) against the angle of the coil (on the *x*-axis).)

Practical 11: Investigation, using a search coil and oscilloscope, of the effect on magnetic flux linkage of varying the angle between a search coil and magnetic field direction

AQA A Level
Physics

Questions

1 How could you reduce the uncertainty in your measurements?

....

....

....

....

....

....

....

....

....

....

....

....

2 What would happen to the flux linkage if the coil radius was doubled?

....

....

....

....

3 Explain why the induced emf decreases as you turn the search coil.

....

....

....

....

....

....

....

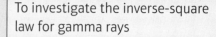

AT a, k, l

CPAC links		Evidence	Done
1a	Correctly follows written instructions to carry out the experimental techniques or procedures.	Practical procedure	
2a	Correctly uses appropriate instrumentation, apparatus and materials (including ICT) to carry out investigative activities, experimental techniques and procedures with minimal assistance or prompting.	Practical procedure	
3b	Uses appropriate safety equipment and approaches to minimise risks with minimal prompting.	Practical procedure	
4a	Makes accurate observations relevant to the experimental or investigative procedure.	Results table	
5a	Uses appropriate software and/or tools to process data, carry out research and report findings.	Processing of data	

Objective

To investigate the inverse-square law for gamma rays

Equipment

- Geiger–Müller tube
- scalar counter
- metre ruler
- stop clock
- sealed gamma source (e.g. cobalt 60 or caesium 137)
- tongs for handling the gamma source

Safety ⚠

- This practical involves a radiation hazard and important rules must be followed. CLEAPSS Guide L93 provides more information.
- Always follow your teacher's instructions carefully.
- Only handle the gamma source using the tongs provided, keeping the active end pointing away from your body (or anyone else's).

Procedure

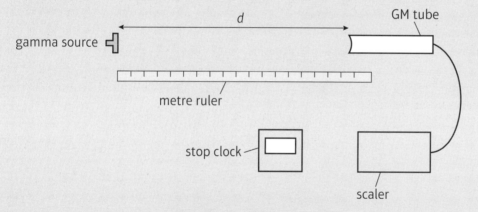

Figure A: Experimental set-up

1 Leave the gamma source in the box and place the Geiger–Müller tube on the bench. Plug it into the scaler. Start the scaler to check it is working.

2 With the gamma source still in its box (and as far away from the apparatus as possible), measure the background radiation, C_0. Switch on the scaler and start a stop clock at the same time. After 20 minutes, record the total counts, N, on the scaler and the time, t.

3 Set up the apparatus as shown in Figure A. Put the source in its holder (not shown in the diagram). Make sure you follow all relevant safety procedures when handing the source.

4 Take some preliminary readings to establish the maximum distance, x, at which the count is above the background value.

5 Place the Geiger–Müller tube 0.70 m from the source ($d = 0.70$ m) – assuming this gives a count rate above background. If not, move the detector closer to the source.

6 Switch on the scaler and start the stop clock at the same time. Record the count, N, after 100 s (t). Repeat two more times and work out the average count rate, C.

7 Repeat steps **5** and **6**, moving the Geiger–Müller tube towards the source in 0.10 m steps until $x = 0.10$ m.

8 Subtract the background count (C_0) from the average count rate (C) to obtain the corrected count rate (C_c).

9 Record N, t, x in a suitable table, including columns for count rate $C = \dfrac{N}{t}$ corrected count rate C_c and $\dfrac{1}{\sqrt{C_c}}$.

Results

Analysis of results

1 Plot a graph with $\frac{1}{\sqrt{C_C}}$ on the y-axis and x on the x-axis. The intensity of gamma radiation decreases with distance according to the inverse-square law. This will be verified if the plot produces a straight line.

Learning tip

The data is plotted this way around (rather that plotting C against $\frac{1}{x^2}$) to eliminate the systematic error in distance measurement. The exact position of the gamma material inside the sealed source, and the position inside the GM tube where ionisation takes place, are not known. The actual distance between the source and the detector, d, is given by $d = x + e$, where e is the systematic error in the distance measurement. This distance, e, can be found from the x-axis intercept on the graph.

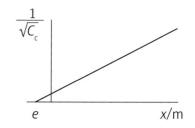

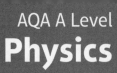

Questions

1 If the source you are using emits both beta and gamma radiation, how can you screen out the beta radiation?

....

....

....

2 Another student suggests that the investigation should be repeated by moving the detector back towards the source in 0.10 m steps. What would you do with the extra data from the repeated measurements?

....

....

....

3 Why would a pure alpha emitter not be suitable for investigating the inverse-square law?

....

....

....

4 Why would you expect to have a different background count in different parts of the country?

....

....

....

....

....

5 What are the most likely major sources of error in this practical?

....

....

....

....

....

....

....

Practical 1: Investigation into the variation of the frequency of stationary waves on a string with length, tension and mass per unit length of the string

1 Suitable answers would be, e.g.
  - Measurement of resonant frequencies will be inaccurate if the calibration of the signal generator is not accurate.
  - Measurement of wavelength is uncertain, because a thick blur is observed at the nodes.

2 The sharpness of resonance is likely to cause the biggest problems. A useful technique is to adjust the frequency while looking closely at the node to gain the largest response. Looking at the amplitude is probably less helpful.

3 Make sure to keep feet away from the masses. Alternatively, keep a tray filled with newspaper under the masses, in case they fall.

Practical 2: Investigation of interference in Young's slit experiment and diffraction by a diffraction grating

1 A resolution of 1 mm is suitable when measuring distances of around 70 cm for the 300 slits/mm grating, and when measuring distances of around 25 cm for the 100 slits/mm grating. This gives percentage uncertainties of 0.1% and 0.4%, respectively.

2 White light is a mixture of frequencies, so the diffraction would be different for each frequency. The maxima are small so, in practice, the inner edge would be tinted blue and the outer edge would be tinted red.

3 Green light has a shorter wavelength than red light, so the fringes would be closer together. The fringe spacing is directly proportional to the wavelength of light used.

4 Suitable answers would be, e.g. uncertainty can be reduced by:
  - using a grating with a smaller line separation
  - increasing the distance between the grating and the screen (but only as long as the pattern is still visible!).

Practical 3: Determination of g by a freefall method

1 Using light gates should mean there is less uncertainty in the time measurements.

2 Air resistance will reduce your value for g.

3 A straight line graph has a constant gradient. The graph of t^2 against h should be a straight line because the gradient depends only on g, which is a constant.

4 A tray of newspapers (or similar) should be placed under the trap door to catch the sphere. This will prevent damage to the floor surface or to the ball, as well as preventing a trip hazard.

5 This value is likely to be constrained by the timings being accurate to 2 significant figures only.

6 a A slight positive value on the y-axis indicates a systematic error. This could be an error in:
  - h – incorrectly measuring the height
  - t – a delay in the timer starting after the sphere is released or a delay in the timer stopping when the trapdoor switch is hit.

  b Drawing the line of best fit correctly will allow you to identify and account for errors (such as the systematic error in part (a)).

Practical 4: Determination of the Young modulus by a simple method

1 The extension is very small and can only be measured to one significant figure using a metre ruler. The mass can be measured more accurately, and you have calculated the gradient of the graph of mass against extension, so you might trust a value to two significant figures. However, it would be more appropriate to give your value for the Young modulus to one significant figure.

2 The wire could break as the masses are added to it; if this happens, it could spring back and hit you.

3 a The second wire is the comparison or control wire. It should be the same length and diameter as the test wire, and made of the same material.

  b The purpose of the control wire is to avoid any errors due to expansion, as both the control wire and the test wire will expand by the same amount. The second wire also compensates for any sagging in the beam.

4 If there are kinks in the wire, the measured extension could be due to the wire straightening out rather than actual extension.

5 A simple check is to remove each weight after the extension has been measured, and measure the length again. If the limit of proportionality has not been exceeded, the length of the wire should return to what it was before the weight was added.

6 The longer and thinner the wire, the greater the extension. The greater the extension, the smaller the effect of any uncertainty in your measurements and the more accurate your value for the Young modulus.

7 Measure the diameter of the wire at different points and in different directions to obtain a mean value for diameter; divide this in two to calculate the radius. Then calculate the cross-sectional area using the formula.

8 Steel does not extend by much, so having a long length of wire suspended vertically will enable you to measure the extension more easily.

Practical 5: Determination of resistivity of a wire using a micrometer, ammeter and voltmeter

1 Ωm

2 The wire may not have a uniform cross-section. Taking readings in different places allows you to find an average value to use when calculating the cross-sectional area.

3 Sources of uncertainty include:
  - Contact resistance between wire and crocodile clip. This could be a random error as the crocodile clip is moved.
  - Resistance between the crocodile clip and the wire at the 'zero' end of the wire. This is a systematic error and would stop the graph passing through the origin.
  - The first crocodile clip may not be at the 'zero' mark. This is also a systematic error.

  All these sources of uncertainty would shift the line of best fit up the graph without altering the gradient. Therefore, they should not affect the accuracy of the calculated value of resistivity.

4 Keeping the current small reduces any heating effects in the wire. The wire must not be allowed to heat up, as resistivity is temperature dependent.

5 A resistor could be added to the circuit, in series with the ammeter and the cell.

Practical 6: Investigation of the emf and internal resistance of electric cells and batteries by measuring the variation of the terminal pd of the cell with current in it

1 The voltmeter does not have an infinite resistance. Any small current will cause a pd across the internal resistance, reducing the terminal pd below the emf.

2 Chemical energy in a battery is used to make electrons move. These electrons collide with atoms inside the battery, and this causes resistance. This is known as internal resistance and is the reason why batteries get warm when they are used.

3 Emf stands for electromotive force; this is the amount of electrical energy produced by the battery for each coulomb of charge. Emf is measured in volts and it is not actually a force. Terminal pd is also measured in volts but it is the potential difference across the load resistance. Terminal pd is the energy transferred through the load resistance when one coulomb of charge flows.

4 'Lost volts' is the energy wasted per coulomb overcoming the internal resistance of the battery.

5 If there was no internal resistance, the emf and the terminal pd would be the same.

Practical 7: Investigation into simple harmonic motion using a mass–spring system and a simple pendulum

Part A: Typical results

A suitable table will have pendulum length as the independent variable and time for 10 oscillations as the dependent variable. The time for one oscillation, T, and T^2 should also be recorded in additional columns. If repeat measurements have been made, the repeats and the mean value of the time for 10 oscillations should be shown.

Sample data

For one pendulum:

l/m	10T/s	T/s	T^2/s^2
0.10	6.3	0.63	0.40
0.20	9.0	0.90	0.81
0.30	11.0	1.10	1.21
0.40	12.7	1.27	1.61
0.50	14.2	1.42	2.02
0.60	15.5	1.55	2.40

This gives the graph shown below.

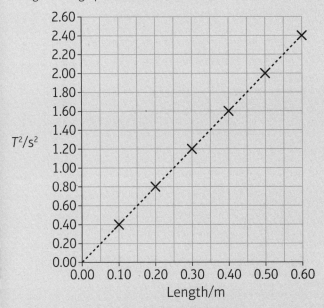

A line of best fit should be drawn for each graph.

For each length, the graph should show the same value of T regardless of the mass, m: the time period of a pendulum is independent of its mass.

For each graph, a straight line through the origin verifies that T^2 is proportional to l.

By measuring the gradient of the graph, you can determine a value for the acceleration due to gravity, g, using the equation $g = \dfrac{4\pi^2}{\text{gradient}}$

The percentage uncertainty in the value of g can be estimated from the uncertainty in your values of l and T, or by finding the gradients of the line of maximum and minimum gradient compared to the gradient of the best fit line:

$$\text{uncertainty} = \text{gradient of best fit line} - \frac{\text{gradient of worst acceptable line}}{}$$

$$\text{percentage uncertainty} = \frac{\text{uncertainty}}{(\text{gradient of best fit line})} \times 100$$

Part A: Answers to questions

1 The equations for simple harmonic motion are only valid for small angular displacements.

2 Zero.

3 At the centre of the oscillation – when the pendulum passes through the centre/above the fiducial marker.

4 When the pendulum is at the top of its swing.

5 When the pendulum is at the bottom of its swing.

6 Galileo discovered that the period of a pendulum is independent of the amplitude or width of the swing. This property – isochronism – makes pendulums useful as timekeepers. Galileo also designed a pendulum clock which his son was to make, although both men died before the clock could be produced.

Part B: Typical results

A suitable table will have pendulum mass as the independent variable and time for 10 oscillations as the dependent variable.

The time for one oscillation, T, and T^2 should also be recorded in additional columns. If repeat measurements have been made, the repeats and the mean value of the time for 10 oscillations should be shown.

Sample data

Mass/kg	T/s	T^2/s^2
0.10	0.59	0.35
0.20	0.84	0.70
0.30	1.03	1.05
0.40	1.19	1.41
0.50	1.33	1.76

This gives the graph:

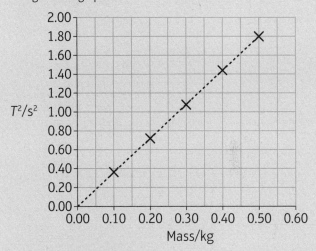

A line of best fit should be drawn.

A straight line through the origin verifies that T^2 is proportional to m.

By measuring the gradient of the graph, you can determine a value for the spring constant, k, using the equation

From this graph, k is found to be 11.23 kg s^{-2}.

Part B: Answers to questions

1 A graph of m against T will produce a curve, whereas a graph of m against T^2 produces a straight line. It is easier to draw a straight line of best fit, rather than a curved one, and easier to find the gradient of a straight line.

2 A tray containing newspaper (or similar) should be placed underneath the masses.

3 To reduce the effect of any errors in timing.

4 The equilibrium point is the point where the mass hangs at rest. The fiducial marker should be placed here because the oscillations will always pass through this point, so this point can be used to count complete oscillations. Placing the fiducial marker at either end of the oscillation will result in errors, because the oscillations will dampen until they no longer pass through these points.

Practical 8: Investigation of Boyle's law (constant temperature) and Charles's law (constant pressure) for a gas

Part A: Sample data

p/kPa	$V/\times 10^{-6}\,m^3$
101	3.41
110	3.13
120	2.87
130	2.65
140	2.46
150	2.29
160	2.15

This gives the graph:

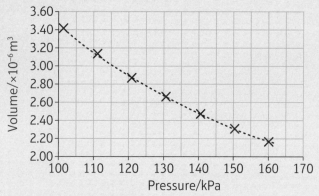

Part A: Answers to questions

1 Ensure the connections are securely in place and avoid excessive pressure, to prevent the oil spraying out of the system.

2 **a** pressure   **b** volume
   c temperature and mass of the air

3 **a** an increase   **b** an increase

4 The air in the tube must not leak out; otherwise the mass will change, and this needs to remain constant. The temperature of the air needs to remain constant, so there should be pauses between readings to allow the gas to cool down.

5 The plot of p against $1/V$ should produce a straight line through the origin. This shows that pressure is inversely proportional to volume, provided the temperature is kept constant. This does confirm Boyle's law.

Part B: Sample data

T/°C	20	30	40	50	60	70	80	90
h/mm	21	21	22	23	23	24	25	26

This gives the graph:

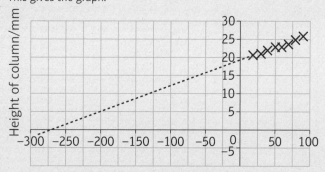

Part B: Answers to questions

1 Add ice cubes to the beaker of water to obtain lower temperatures. This would produce a greater range of values.

2 If the air contains moisture, the approximation to an ideal gas fails.

3 The top of the capillary tube above the droplet of sulfuric acid or mercury is open, so the pressure of the trapped air is due to atmospheric pressure and the weight of the droplet of sulfuric acid or mercury. It is a valid assumption that neither atmospheric pressure nor the weight of the droplet of sulfuric acid or mercury will change during the experiment.

4 As a real gas cools, it will condense to a liquid.

5 Absolute zero is −273.15 °C. This is the temperature at which all the fundamental particles of nature have minimal vibrational motion.

6 This will depend on your results.

7 There are several common issues with the experiment:
   • The seal at the base of the capillary tube could have a small leak.
   • The negative extrapolation required to obtain a value of absolute zero requires a lengthy x-axis but with only a limited plot of values to produce the line.
   • The temperature of the air inside the capillary tube may not be the same as the measured temperature of the water.

Practical 9: Investigation of the charge and discharge of capacitors

Analysis techniques should include log-linear plotting leading to a determination of the time constant, RC

1 RC is the time constant for the discharge. It is the time taken for the voltage across the capacitor to fall to $1/e$ of its initial value. This gives an order of magnitude for the time scale for the capacitor to discharge.

2 This means the values may not be completely accurate, due to manufacturing tolerances which produce variance in the components produced.

3 The second graph produces a straight line. This effectively averages several readings and it is easier to gain further data from a straight line graph than an exponential decay curve.

4 The computer and data logger would record the data, process the results and produce graphs for you. You would be able to take many more readings and there would be less chance of errors (since you would not have to try to read time and pd at the same time).

Practical 10: Investigation into how the force on a wire varies with flux density, current and length of wire using a top pan balance

1 Accept any suitable answers, e.g.
   • There is an edge effect to the magnetic field/the magnetic field is weaker towards the ends of the field/the magnetic field is not uniform.
   • The wire may have been affected by additional magnetic fields which are produced where the wire connects to the main circuit.

2 The formula $F = BIL$ is only valid if the current is perpendicular to the field lines.

3 Magnetic flux density is the force on one metre of wire carrying a current of one amp at right angles to a magnetic field. It is measured in tesla, T.

4 This ensures that the mass reading is only due to the electromagnetic force.

Practical 11: Investigation, using a search coil and oscilloscope, of the effect on magnetic flux linkage of varying the angle between a search coil and magnetic field direction

1 Suitable suggestions, e.g.
   • It can be difficult to measure the angle of the coil. Take repeated readings of the emf and calculate a mean value for each angle.
   • Add an ammeter and a variable resistor to the circuit to ensure the current remains constant. This will ensure the amplitude of the magnetic field is also kept constant.

2 If the coil radius is doubled, the flux linkage will increase by a factor of four.

3 The emf decreases because the search coil is cutting fewer flux lines. This is because the component of the magnetic field that is perpendicular to the area of the coil gets lower, so the total magnetic flux passing through the coil is lower. The coil will experience a lower magnetic flux linkage.

Practical 12: Investigation of the inverse-square law for gamma radiation

1 Place a thin sheet of aluminium directly in front of the source. This will stop beta particles, but gamma rays will pass through.

2 Plot both sets of data on the same graph to allow a comparison.

3 Alpha radiation does not follow the inverse-square law because it is strongly absorbed by the air.

4 About half the background count is from radon gas, with another quarter from other ground sources and buildings. These factors depend on the ground beneath you. For example, parts of Cornwall and Devon have particularly high background counts.

5 The main error is a systematic error in distance measurement. The distance, d, is measured to the front of the tube, not to the point at which detection takes place; we should really use $(d + e)$ for the measurement, where e is a constant. The gamma emitting material is also set back inside the sealed source, which adds to the distance error.
   In addition, the tube will have some dead time where it misses counts. This becomes very important for small count rates.

Practical 1

- Understand the relationship between degrees and radians and translate from one to the other
- Plot two variables from experimental or other data

Practical 2

- Plot two variables from experimental or other data
- Determine the slope and intercept of a linear graph
- Use of small angle approximations including $\sin \theta \cong \theta$, $\tan \theta \cong \theta$, $\cos \theta \cong 1$ for small θ where appropriate
- Find arithmetic means
- Identify uncertainties in measurements and use simple techniques to determine uncertainty where data are combined by addition, subtraction, multiplication, division and raising to powers

Practical 3

- Use ratios, fractions and percentages
- Find arithmetic means
- Distinguish between instantaneous rate of change and average rate of change
- Apply the concepts underlying calculus (but without requiring the explicit use of derivatives or integrals) by solving equations involving rates of change, eg $\delta x/\delta t = -\lambda x$ using a graphical method or spreadsheet modelling
- Plot two variables from experimental or other data
- Understand that $y = mx + c$ represents a linear relationship
- Determine the slope and intercept of a linear graph
- Identify uncertainties in measurements and use simple techniques to determine uncertainty where data are combined by addition, subtraction, multiplication, division and raising to powers

Practical 4

- Translate information between graphical, numerical and algebraic forms
- Plot two variables from experimental or other data
- Determine the slope and intercept of a linear graph
- Identify uncertainties in measurements and use simple techniques to determine uncertainty where data are combined by addition, subtraction, multiplication, division and raising to powers
- Use an appropriate number of significant figures
- Calculate the circumferences, surface areas and volumes of regular shapes

Practical 5

- Plot two variables from experimental or other data
- Use sin, cos and tan in physical problems
- Calculate the circumferences, surface areas and volumes of regular shapes
- Find arithmetic means
- Substitute numerical values into algebraic equations using appropriate units for physical quantities
- Plot two variables from experimental or other data

- Determine the slope and intercept of a linear graph
- Identify uncertainties in measurements and use simple techniques to determine uncertainty where data are combined by addition, subtraction, multiplication, division and raising to powers

Practical 6

- Translate information between graphical, numerical and algebraic forms
- Draw and use the slope of a tangent to a curve as a measure of rate of change
- Plot two variables from experimental or other data
- Understand that $y = mx + c$ represents a linear relationship
- Determine the slope and intercept of a linear graph

Practical 7

- Use of small angle approximations including $\sin \theta \cong \theta$, $\tan \theta \cong \theta$, $\cos \theta \cong 1$ for small θ where appropriate
- Find arithmetic means
- Plot two variables from experimental or other data
- Determine the slope and intercept of a linear graph
- Substitute numerical values into algebraic equations using appropriate units for physical quantities
- Identify uncertainties in measurements and use simple techniques to determine uncertainty where data are combined by addition, subtraction, multiplication, division and raising to powers

Practical 8

- Plot two variables from experimental or other data
- Understand that $y = mx + c$ represents a linear relationship
- Determine the slope and intercept of a linear graph
- Use ratios, fractions and percentages

Practical 9

- Understand the possible physical significance of the area between a curve and the x axis and be able to calculate it by graphical methods as appropriate
- Interpret logarithmic plots
- Use logarithmic plots to test exponential and power law variations
- Plot two variables from experimental or other data
- Determine the slope and intercept of a linear graph

Practical 10

- Plot two variables from experimental or other data
- Determine the slope and intercept of a linear graph
- Substitute numerical values into algebraic equations using appropriate units for physical quantities

Practical 11

- Plot two variables from experimental or other data

Practical 12

- Sketch relationships which are modelled by $y = \frac{k}{x}$, $y = kx^2$, $y = \frac{k}{x^2}$, $y = kx$, $y = \sin x$, $y = \cos x$, $y = e^{\pm x}$ and $y = \sin^2 x$, $y = \cos^2 x$ as applied to physical relationships

- Plot two variables from experimental or other data

- Understand that $y = mx + c$ represents a linear relationship

- Determine the slope and intercept of a linear graph